The Fun Trivia Questions Book

A Small but Mighty General Knowledge Quiz about Random Facts

Zach Olson

Table of Contents

Introduction.. 01

All Around the World..02

Science and Crazy Numbers 13

Fun with Words 19

Food and Drinks Trivia...26

The Wildlife...32

Humorous History 42

Famous and Not-So-Famous People...............49

7 Bonus Questions...61

Conclusion...65

Sources 66

Introduction

Hey, my name is Zach. I love learning new things, and in my opinion, one of the best ways to do so is by doing quizzes. It is a perfect way to discover new facts and also have fun in the process. And that's exactly why I've put together this small book of random but entertaining trivia questions.

While reading or quizzing, you will learn a lot of trivia you didn't know, trivia you never thought about, and trivia you're not sure you want to know. But *The Fun Trivia Questions Book* is more than just a list of questions and answers. For each fact, I give you further background information to tell you the whole story. It is fun for all ages, and you can use it for family game night, when you are on the plane, at the dinner table, at a campfire... just whenever you've got nothing but time.

There are only so many movies to watch, and the trivia inside this book will keep you entertained and fill you up with knowledge. I hope you'll enjoy it!

All Around the World

1. Where are Albert Einstein's eyeballs?
A) In his hometown Ulm, in Germany
B) In Switzerland
C) In New York City

In New York City.
The story of Albert Einstein's remains begins shortly after his death in 1955 at Princeton Hospital. There, the hospital's pathologist Thomas Harvey performed an illegal autopsy. Harvey then requested and received a "retroactive blessing" from Einstein's son, Hans Albert, with an understanding that any research conducted would be for scientific purposes. Although Einstein had specific instructions for his remains: "Burn them and secretly disperse the ashes to discourage idolaters," clearly the opposite happened. Harvey preserved Einstein's brain (split it up into anywhere from 170 to over 200 pieces) while also removing his eyeballs. He gave them to Einstein's ophthalmologist Henry Abrams. They are kept in a safe in New York City to this day.

2. Where does McDonald's serve spaghetti?
A) In Russia
B) In China
C) In the Philippines

In the Philippines.
McDonald's is known for its classic American fast-food cuisine. Customers love their chicken nuggets, French fries, shakes, and

Big Macs. When you think of McDonald's, these are usually the meals that come to mind. However, in the Philippines, McDonald's also sells the most unexpected dinner: pasta. Yes, McDonald's sells a dish called McSpaghetti. For me, McDonald's and Italian food don't seem like a great mix, but hey–it must be working for some people! According to PopSugar, the McDonald's version of spaghetti is served in a box with the long noodles topped with a generous serving of tomato sauce and shredded cheese. The marinara-like sauce is topped with either ground beef or pieces of sausage that resemble sliced hot dogs. You can even order the McSpaghetti with a fried chicken leg. Sounds delicious, doesn't it?

3. Which famous landmark used to be a lighthouse?
A) The Statue of Liberty
B) The London Bridge
C) The Eiffel Tower

The Statue of Liberty.
Everyone knows the Statue of Liberty as a symbol of the freedom of America, but few are probably aware that many years earlier, it had been an official lighthouse that operated under the supervision of the Lighthouse Board. The burning torch in Lady Liberty's right hand, which still has great symbolic significance, was initially also used as a navigation aid for ships entering New York Harbor. The statue was first lit at 7:35 p.m. on November 1st, 1886, and was put into operation as a lighthouse on November 22nd.

4. Where is the one Starbucks where baristas aren't allowed to write names on the cups?
A) In Las Vegas
B) In the CIA headquarters
C) In the Starbucks Reserve Roastery, Seattle

In the CIA headquarters.

There's only one Starbucks in the world that there's no chance your name will be misspelled on a cup: The one located at the CIA headquarters in Langley, Virginia. No names grace the cups here, much to the frustration of a food service supervisor who complained that things might move faster if they did. And, according to the newspaper, there are tons of people to serve. The place is described as one of the busiest Starbucks in America, with lines that can snake down the hallway.

5. In which city is it illegal to do "fancy riding" on bikes?
   A) In Brisbane, Australia
   B) In Glaseburg, Illinois
   C) In Edinburgh, Scotland

In Galesburg, Illinois.

Yes, it's true, you can look it up in the Galesburg Code of Ordinances. It says, "No rider of a bicycle shall remove both hands from the handlebars, or feet from the pedals, or practice any acrobatic or fancy riding on any street." You'd better not try it out!

6. Where's the shortest railway in the world?
   A) In Sweden
   B) In England
   C) In Japan

In England.

According to the Guinness Book of Records, the shortest funicular railway is the Fisherman's Walk Cliff Railway in Bournemouth. Built in 1935, the 128-foot (39-meter) railway has a vertical height of 9 feet (3 meters) and serves millions of people who visit Bournemouth's stunning beaches each year. Taking into account weight, temperature, and wind speed, the journey takes about a minute.

7. Does the moon have active volcanoes?

A) Yes, it does

B) No, and it never did

C) No, but it did at one time

No, but it did at one time.

NASA's Lunar Reconnaissance Orbiter (LRO) has provided researchers with strong evidence that the moon's volcanic activity gradually slowed down billions of years ago. Some volcanic deposits are estimated to be 100 million years old, meaning that the moon was ejecting lava when dinosaurs from the Cretaceous period were busy swatting giant dragonflies. There is even evidence of 50-million-year-old volcanism–practically yesterday by lunar standards.

8. Were the pubs always open on Saint Patrick's Day in Ireland?

A) Yes

B) No

C) It is not known

No! You couldn't imagine it today, but, until the 1970s, pubs in Ireland were closed on Saint Patrick's Day.

St. Patrick's Day is associated with many things: wearing green, breaking Lent, going to a parade, and of course, drowning the shamrock. There is no other day of the year when the "drunken

Irish" stereotype is more pronounced–and used by some as an excuse to enjoy themselves a bit too much–than on March 17th. In Ireland, this day marks the death of the country's beloved patron saint and has been celebrated as a religious feast day for over a thousand years. This is why, until the 1970s, Irish law banned pubs from opening on March 17th as a sign of respect for this religious day. It was feared that opening the pubs would be too tempting for some during Lent and lead to disrespectful drunkenness on this most solemn day.

9. **Which is the only US State capital without a single McDonald's?**
   A) Juneau, Alaska
   B) Montpelier, Vermont
   C) Santa Fe, New Mexico

Montpelier, Vermont.

When traveling to a big city in the US (or most other countries), it seems like there is a McDonald's on every street corner. But not in Montpelier, the state capital of Vermont. To be fair, it's not as glaring an omission as it might seem. Montpelier is the smallest state capital, in terms of population, with only around 7,500 inhabitants. It also prefers local businesses over large chains, so McDonald's should not take this personally. The city doesn't have a Burger King, either.

10. **What percentage of the Sahara Desert is sandy?**
    A) approximately 25 percent
    B) approximately 55 percent
    C) approximately 95 percent

Approximately 25 percent.
The Sahara is the largest hot desert in the world. It is located in North Africa and covers large parts of the continent: 3,320,000 square miles (8,600,000 square kilometers), which is comparable to the size of China or the USA. Sand dunes only cover about 25 percent of the actual surface of the Sahara. The desert also has numerous other land features, including salt flats, gravel plains, plateaus, and even mountains where snow has been recorded.

11. Where is the only Shell gas station that is shaped like a shell?

A) In Bournemouth, England

B) In Winston-Salem, North Carolina

C) In Tucson, Arizona

In Winston-Salem, North Carolina.
There were once eight shell-shaped gas stations in North Carolina: seven in Winston-Salem and one in nearby Kernersville. These Shell Oil gas stations were built in the 1930s by a local distributor of Shell Oil and were intended to serve as hard-to-miss advertisements to entice customers to drop by. Wouldn't you choose to get your gas from a fun place like this over an old, boring, normal gas station? Today, only one of these Shell stations is left. The final remaining clamshell station is on the corner of East Sprague and Peachtree Streets in Winston-Salem. You can still stop at the glorious yellow-stuccoed street attraction to take photos, but don't show up with an empty tank: It's no longer a working gas station! The station closed in the 1950s and briefly housed a lawnmower store in the 1970s and 1980s. But today, the shell is only for show. Just because the old Shell gas station lost its function doesn't mean this North Carolina roadside attraction will disappear soon—it was added to the National Register of Historic Places in 1976.

12. What colors do passports around the world come in?
A) Black, red, yellow, and blue
B) Black, red, white, and blue
C) Black, red, green, and blue

Black, red, green, and blue.
Passports are only made in four colors: black, blue, red, and green. Surprisingly, there are no official rules or regulations governing what colors passports have to be. Countries are free to choose any color they want, and there are many variations in the shades of blue, black, green, and red used for passports. But why are passports available in these colors? Probably, because they look the most official. The dark colors also hide signs of dirt and wear and tear. Countries choose them because they look more official than, for example, neon pink. The color that a country chooses can be determined by both culture and historical significance. For example, the color green has a religious meaning for Islamic countries. Burgundy–a shade of red–is the preferred color for countries in the European Union, while India has a blue passport. However, there are certain rules that all countries must follow: passports should be made of a material that can bend, won't wrinkle, and can withstand chemicals, extreme temperatures, humidity, and light.

13. Where is the world's largest national park located?
A) In Russia
B) In Canada
C) In Greenland

In Greenland.
With an area of 375,000 square miles (972,000 square kilometers),

the Greenland National Park is the largest in the world. The area is almost the size of France and Spain combined and includes the entire northeastern part of Greenland. The coast is 11,000 miles (18,000 kilometers) long and includes both the highest parts of the largest ice cap in the northern hemisphere and the northernmost area of land. Various Inuit cultures have lived and survived here for thousands of years, thanks to the high number of Arctic species.

14. Where are shadows darker, on the Earth or on the moon?

A) On the Earth
B) On the moon
C) They are equally dark

On the moon.

On Earth, the movement of living things, the changes in the natural and cultural environments, and the weather which traps the sunlight to varying degrees make the shadows very dynamic. Air scatters light and allows objects not exposed to direct sunlight to be well lit. This is an effect called Rayleigh scattering, named after the British Nobel Prize winner Lord Rayleigh (John William Strutt). Rayleigh scattering is why the skies are blue and why you can still read a magazine perfectly well under an umbrella on the beach. However, as there is no air on the moon, there is no Rayleigh scattering. So shadows are very dark and it is very bright where sunlight comes in. Areas of shadow are dramatically cloudy, but some light is still reflected in them–this is due to reflected light from the lunar surface itself.

15. How long did it take to build the Eiffel Tower?

A) 1 years, 3 months, and 7 days
B) 2 years, 2 months, and 5 days
C) 3 years, 1 month, and 4 days

2 years, 2 months, and 5 days.
On June 12th, 1886, the decision was made to build the iron tower proposed by Gustave Eiffel during the competition for the Exposition Universelle, which was to be opened on May 15th, 1889. That only left him 3 years to build the tower. Additionally, it took another 6 months to obtain the country's concession from the city of Paris for negotiations with the state. Work began in January 1887 with the construction of sixteen masonry foundation blocks, one per edge. The foundations were completed 6 months later, and assembly of the metal structure began in July 1887. There were less than 2 years left to build the tower, but they managed to finish it on time. The secret of this rapid assembly was the complete prefabrication of the tower's 12,000 parts in Eiffel's workshops in Levallois-Perret, which had already begun during the construction of the foundations. There, all the parts were calculated, drawn, cut, drilled, and pre-assembled with rivets, then sent to the construction site and returned to the workshop in the case of defects. Two-thirds of the tower's 2,500,000 or so rivets were set in the factory. Modest steam cranes and between 150 and 300 well-supervised workers were enough to assemble all the prefabricated metal parts in 22 months. What a masterfully executed project!

---

16. Where is the largest waterfall in the world?
A) In the USA
B) In Canada
C) In the ocean

In the ocean. More specifically, in the ocean between Greenland and Iceland.
Rivers that flow over the gorges of the Earth form waterfalls that are natural wonders and attract millions of visitors due to their breathtaking beauty, size, and power. But no waterfall is larger or more powerful than those that lie beneath the ocean (yes beneath!) and cascade over immense cataracts hidden from our view. In fact, the world's largest waterfall lies beneath the Strait of Denmark, which separates Iceland and Greenland. At the lower

end of the strait is a series of cataracts that start 2,000 feet (600 meters) below the surface of the strait and descend to a depth of 10,000 feet (3 kilometers) on the southern tip of Greenland–nearly a two-mile drop. But how can there be waterfalls in the ocean? This is because cold water is denser than warm water and, in the Strait from Denmark, southward-flowing frigid water from the Nordic Seas meets warmer water from the Irminger Sea. The cold, dense water quickly sinks below the warmer water and flows over the giant drops of the ocean floor, creating a downward flow.

17. Where did a woman call the police because her ice cream didn't have enough sprinkles?
A) In Denmark
B) In the USA
C) In England

In England.
West Midlands Police in England released a record of a woman calling the emergency number to help in an argument about sprinkles on her ice cream. She contacted the police after arguing with the owner of an ice cream truck. During the minute-long call, she said to the emergency services: "It doesn't seem like a major emergency, but it is a little bit because I ordered an ice cream, and he's put bits on one side but none on the other. He refuses to give me my money back and says I have to take it like that." Chief Superintendent Jim Andronov warned against abusing the emergency system. If someone is trying to report a real life-or-death emergency, one minute is a very long wait. He added that about 50 percent of calls to the 999 operators are not emergency calls. For example, in another case, a caller wanted to seek help after forgetting his Facebook password!

18. Why is there no airport in the country Andorra?

A) Because the country is too small

B) Because there are too many mountains

C) Because there are not enough inhabitants

Because there are too many mountains.

Airports have become symbols of economic and social progress. As a means of transport, it has advantages that others simply cannot offer. The speed, distance, and connections that airplanes and airports offer are second to none. This is why it is so rare to find a country without an airport. But there are some, for example, Andorra. The Principality of Andorra is not as small as you might think. Its surface area is 180 square miles (468 square kilometers), so there's room for several airports, but the problem here is the mountains. The co-principality lies between Spain and France and is isolated from the rest of Europe by the Pyrenees that completely surround it, peaks that are nearly 10,000 feet (3,000 meters) high. At such altitudes, modern aviation is difficult and dangerous, especially when fog or ice is added to the equation. And that's why the Andorra-La Seu d'Urgell Airport is located in Spain, 10.8 miles (17.4 kilometers) from the border with Andorra.

Science and Crazy Numbers

19. What's the highest denomination note ever printed?

A) The $10,000 gold certificate bill

B) The $100,000 gold certificate bill

C) The $100,000,000 gold certificate bill

The $100,000 gold certificate bill.
The $100,000 bill with the portrait of President Woodrow Wilson was actually a gold certificate that was never circulated or issued for public use. The Bureau of Engraving and Printing produced it in 1934 during the Great Depression to conduct official transactions between Federal Reserve banks. Only 42,000 of the $100,000 bills were ever printed. While the $100,000 bill cannot be legally kept by collectors, some institutions such as the Museum of American Finance issue them for educational purposes. The Smithsonian Museum and some branches of the Federal Reserve System (FRS) also hold these rare bills. Their value today is estimated at about $1.6 million.

20. What's the normal operating engine temperature of a car?

A) Between 90 and 104 degrees Celsius (195 and 220 degrees Fahrenheit)

B) Between 85 and 99 degrees Celsius (185 and 210 degrees Fahrenheit)

C) Between 79 and 93 degrees Celsius (175 and 200 degrees Fahrenheit)

Between 90 and 104 degrees Celsius (195 and 220 degrees Fahrenheit).

Most modern vehicles have a display that shows a constant temperature value of the coolant circulating in the engine in order to give the driver an early warning of a problem in the cooling system. For most automobiles, the normal engine temperature is in the range of 90 to 104 degrees Celsius (195 to 220 degrees Fahrenheit). On average, the temperature needle is at or near the center when the engine is at normal operating temperature, which usually takes at least a minute or two to reach after starting a cold engine. Using the air conditioning at full power, stop-and-go driving on a scorching day, and towing may raise the engine temperature above normal. Don't panic if the display changes slightly. You can pull off the street for a while or turn off the air conditioning and turn on the heater to cool things down. Yes, you read correctly; turning on the heater will cool down the engine.

21. Who invented a car controlled by a joystick?

A) Ferrari

B) Mercedes

C) Ford

Mercedes.

As the name suggests, the "Mercedes F200 Imagination" was not only a visionary and innovative proposal from Mercedes-Benz but also an extremely ambitious project. Its most important feature is the future-oriented dynamic handling system "Drive-by-Wire" with which the driver could control the entire vehicle movement with a joystick. Steering was done by moving the joystick in the desired direction; pushing the control stick forward accelerated the vehicle, and pulling back applied the brakes. The steering wheel and pedals are removed, which means that the passengers have more space and, therefore, more comfort.

22. What household appliance inspired one of the first pairs of Nikes?
A) A refrigerator
B) A toaster
C) A waffle iron

A waffle iron.
The co-founder of Nike, Bill Bowerman, who was a legendary track and field coach at the University of Oregon, made the white waffle spike shoes for one of his runners at the school. They were made in the early 1970s and modified in 1974 to add the "waffle sole," a major innovation in Nike history. Bowerman invented the design after taking inspiration from his wife's waffle maker. He partnered with former Oregon runner Phil Knight in 1964 to create Blue Ribbon Sports. In 1971, the two renamed their business Nike and started a company that would eventually dominate the global sportswear market. In 2019, the legendary waffle sneakers were auctioned at an astonishing $475,500.

23. Which building grows more than 6 inches (15 centimeters) during the summer?
A) The Burj Khalifa Tower
B) The Eiffel Tower
C) The Leaning Tower of Pisa

The Eiffel Tower.
Until 1930, the Eiffel Tower was the tallest building in the world. Named after its founder Gustave Eiffel, it was intended to set an example for the French Revolution and function as a radio transmission tower. The Eiffel Tower gets up to 6 inches (15 centimeters) higher in summer when the temperature reaches 40 degrees Celsius (104 degrees Fahrenheit). Extreme heat expands the metal at the base and increases the height of the 1,000-foot (320-meter) tower.

24. At what temperature do tennis balls need to be stored for the Wimbledon tournament?

A) At 18 degrees Celsius (64 degrees Fahrenheit)

B) At 20 degrees Celsius (68 degrees Fahrenheit)

C) At 22 degrees Celsius (71 degrees Fahrenheit)

At 20 degrees Celsius (68 degrees Fahrenheit).

During each tournament at Wimbledon, 54,250 balls are used. They are swapped out every seven to nine games. Because of the effect of temperature on the ball performance, all balls are stored at 20 degrees Celsius (68 degrees Fahrenheit), and each one is tested for bounce and weight. Inside a tennis ball is a hollow core that contains gas. If the temperature of the ball changes, the pressure of the gas inside changes, which influences the ball's physical dynamics.

25. Which is the biggest single-celled organism?

A) Caulera faxifolia

B) Caulerpa taxifolia

C) Caulepa taxifoli

Caulerpa taxifolia.

Caulerpa taxifolia is a green algae and species of seaweed that can become up to 12 inches (30 centimeters) long. It is considered to be the largest single-celled organism in the world. Its surface is enhanced by a frond-like structure, and it is coenocytic, which means that it's a single cell with multiple nuclei. This makes it like a multicellular organism but without the division between cells.

26. How can new equipment for the Space Station be up there within seconds?

A) Thanks to extremely fast rockets

B) Thanks to teleportation

C) Thanks to 3D print technology

Thanks to 3D print technology.

It used to take months or even years to get new equipment to the space station, depending on the replenishment schedule. Nowadays, tools can be printed out in the space station. Many of the specifications for the equipment were preprogrammed into the 3D printer before it left Earth, while others are sent as files from Earth into space. Sending a file to the station is as quick as sending an email. The technology opens up opportunities to create objects that could not even be brought into space before.

27. How long is the shortest passenger flight in the world?

A) 90 seconds

B) 120 seconds

C) 180 seconds

90 seconds.

It could very well take longer to read this story than flying on the world's shortest scheduled flight. Loganair, a Scottish regional airline, holds this title thanks to its route between Westray and Papa Westray, two of the Orkney Islands north of Great Britain. The cost of a one-way ticket starts at £17 (about $22) and the flight, which travels 1.7 miles (2.7 kilometers), takes only 1.5 minutes in the air. This seems like nothing compared to the 19-hour flight of the Australian airline Qantas. The 10,200-mile (16,200-kilometer) non-stop trip from New York to Sydney is the longest flight in the world.

28. Does bleach expire?

A) Yes

B) No

C) I don't know

Yes, after about 1 year.

Bleach is very effective at killing germs and viruses and disinfecting all types of surfaces at home. However, it is only effective if it has not expired. The bleach actually begins to degrade or break down about six months after the date of manufacture. After six months, the concentration of bleach is lower than when it was first made, but it can be effectively used for disinfecting for up to a year. When bleach degrades, it breaks down into water, salt, and oxygen. Hence, it is not effective for sanitizing anymore.

29. Which organization tests its product's durability with a butt-shaped robot?

A) IKEA

B) Samsung

C) Tommy Hilfiger

Samsung.

Deep inside Samsung's headquarters in Suwon, South Korea, countless employees spend most of the day putting the company's latest cell phones through a series of grueling, wincing durability tests. Before a Samsung smartphone can hit the market, the electronics giant wants to make sure that it can withstand a significant beating and continue to function properly.

Fun with Words

30. Which came first: Orange the color or orange the fruit?

A) Orange the color

B) Orange the fruit

C) This is not known

Orange the fruit.
The citrus fruit got named orange first. The word for the fruit originated from old French, and the first time it was recorded in English dates back to the 1300s. The word's use as the name of a color appears in the early 1500s, 200 years later. As oranges were widely available on the market, people started to also use the word for the color. Before then, English speakers referred to the color orange as "yellow-red."

31. What does the clothes store H&M stand for?

A) Haus & Mode

B) Her & Him

C) Hennes & Mauritz

Hennes & Mauritz.
The origins of this Swedish brand go back to the 1940s, according to the H&M website. It was in 1947 when Erling Persson, a Swedish entrepreneur, opened a women's clothing store. This store, located in Sweden, was called Hennes, which means "Hers" in English. In 1968, Hennes decided to buy "Mauritz Widforss," a retailer of hunting and fishing clothing and equipment.

Unfortunately, there's no fancy Swedish meaning for Mauritz other than the name of the man who originally started the brand.

32. Was the dunce cap always a visual symbol of idiocy and punishment?
A) Yes
B) No
C) What's a dunce cap?

No—let me explain.
Nowadays, few people refer to dunce caps anymore. The caps themselves were usually made from rolling paper into a cone and writing a "D" or the word dunce/fool on the paper to indicate to viewers that the person wearing the cap had done something remarkably stupid. It is known as a dunce cap, dunce's cap, dunce hat, or dunce's hat. But, it turns out that the origin of the fool cap is filled with irony. The dunce cap was once viewed as something closer to a wizard's hat. While we understand today that the goofy-looking cone hat signified some kind of intellectual failure, it actually began as a symbol of respected scholars.

33. Where does the abbreviation Xmas come from?
A) From the Greek
B) From the Hebrew
C) From the Roman

From the Greek.
The history of the word Christmas is actually more fascinating than you might think. First of all, the abbreviation is way older (centuries) than its use in bright advertisements. It was first used in the mid-16th century. X stands for the Greek letter "Chi," the first letter of the word "Χριστός" (Chrīstos), which means Jesus

Christ. That's why X has been an acceptable representation of the word Christ for hundreds of years which therefore led to the word Xmas.

34. What do you call a flock of ravens?
A) An unkindness
B) An ominousness
C) An airsickness

An unkindness.
There is speculation about the origin of the term. Some suggest that it goes back to the creature's symbolic association with witches and death. Others refer to the ravens' "kleptomaniac habits" when it comes to other birds' eggs. In light of recent findings, however, the collective name could be seen as unkind in itself. Scientists at the Institute for Research on Wildlife Resources (IREC) found that ravens have a significantly lower impact on the population growth of their prey than other predators. Whether this means they are unfairly maligned is a matter of opinion, but one thing is certain: These winged creatures are highly intelligent and possess strong social skills. They are able to recognize the dynamics within a group, even if they have never belonged to it. The only other creatures known to be capable of this are humans.

35. Which letter does not appear in any US state name?
A) The letter J
B) The letter Q
C) The letter Z

The letter Q.
Only one letter? Yes, only Q isn't contained in any US state name.

Every other letter of the alphabet appears at least once. Fifty different names and not one of them contains the letter Q. I bet many of you guessed J, X, or Z, as these letters also seem very rare. And you're right, they are. But if you said they don't appear in any state name, you probably don't live in New Jersey, Texas, or Arizona.

36. What is a cow-bison hybrid called?

A) A "Bicow"

B) A "Beefalo"

C) A "Buffcattle"

A "Beefalo."

There are many benefits to crossing a cow with a bison. USDA testing showed that beefalo possess superior vitamin levels, higher protein, less cholesterol, 79 percent less fat, and 66 percent fewer calories than conventional beef. Also, beefalo cuts have received the "Best Steak" award at the American Royal Steak Competition for several years in a row. And last but not least, it is famous for being a healthier beef for you and the world.

37. How many words and expressions for snow exist in Scotland?

A) 251

B) 379

C) 421

421.

Academics have officially registered 421 snow-terms that Scots use—including "skelf" (a large snowflake), "sneesl" (to begin to snow), "snaw" (snow), and more. Researchers propose that this variety of terms originated from the ancestors of the Scottish people. It shows the importance for them to communicate about the weather which could easily affect their livelihood. Here are some more cool expressions: "feefle" (to swirl), "flindrikin" (a slight snow shower), "snaw-pouther" (fine driving snow), "spitters" (small drops or flakes of wind-driven rain or snow), and "unbrak" (the beginning of a thaw).

38. What is the unique ant species in New York called?
A) TimesSquareAnts
B) ManhattAnts
C) YorkAnts

They are called ManhattAnts.
The residents of Manhattan are arguably a breed all their own. The same goes for their ants. Especially somewhere between 63rd and 76th Streets, where biologists have discovered a completely new species of ant. "It's new to North America, and we believe it's new to the whole world," said Rob Dunn, the professor of biology whose team discovered the insect. The Big Apple insects were tentatively named "ManhattAnts" until a more scientific nomenclature could be arranged. It's a relative of the cornfield ant, and it looks like it originated in Europe.

39. What was the last letter added to the alphabet? And no, it's not Z.
A) J
B) Q
C) Y

It's J.
It's no coincidence that I and J are next to each other in the

alphabet–they were considered the same character for centuries! The letter J began as a swing letter, a typographic embellishment for the pre-existing I, which was used to mark the end of a series of ones–as in "Henry viij" for Henry the 8th. Both I and J were used interchangeably to express the sound of both the vowel and the consonant until the Renaissance grammarian Gian Giorgio Trissino argued for the independence of the poor letter J in 1524. After being snubbed for nearly three centuries, J was finally recognized as a full-fledged letter in the 19th century, making it the baby of the English alphabet.

40. Where does the word "OK" come from?
A) from the words "all correct"
B) from the words "oh key"
C) from the words "alright clear"

It comes from the words "all correct."
We say it and type it countless times a day, but have you ever thought about what "OK" actually stands for? And is it right to write "OK" or is it "okay"? People know what the word means– it's a verbal thumbs-up to indicate approval–but for most of us, where this unique expression comes from is a mystery. If you go through the trouble of typing two extra characters to spell "okay," you're technically wrong. It's more correct to write "OK" because it's actually an acronym from the 19th century. OK stands for "oll correct" or "all correct." Back then, it was part of a trend for writers to playfully misspell and abbreviate their words, just for fun. They were even more creative with abbreviations than they are today, LOL.

41. What is an anagram for Albert Einstein?
A) Ten elite brains
B) The elite brain
C) Elite brain test

Ten elite brains.

It seems incredibly appropriate that the genius Albert Einstein's name is an anagram of the phrase "ten elite brains." Meaning that the exact same letters are used for his name and the phrase but differently arranged. It is also an anagram for "elite brain nest" and "brainliest teen." Coincidence?

Food and Drinks Trivia

42. How old is the oldest wine?

A) At least 1,000 years old

B) At least 1,350 years old

C) At least 1,650 years old

At least 1,650 years old.

Wine has a long and rich history in human existence that predates even written records. One theory postulates that the fermentation of alcohol took off between 10,000 and 8,000 BC. But, unfortunately, we don't have bottles from that early era anymore. The oldest bottle of wine, known as "Römerwein" or "The Speyer Wine Bottle," is at least 1,650 years old. This goes back to the 4th century, sometime between 325 and 359 AD. The 1.5-liter glass vessel was discovered during the excavation of a Roman aristocratic grave in modern-day Germany. If you're wondering how this old wine smells or even tastes—we don't know. Experts are uncertain what would happen to the liquid if it were exposed to air. So it has remained sealed with its thick stopper made of wax and olive oil since then.

43. What are the different flavors of "Froot Loops?"

A) lime, orange, grape, lemon, cherry, and strawberry

B) lime, orange, grape, lemon, cherry, and raspberry

C) There are no different flavors

There are no different flavors, they all taste the same.

I hate to tell you this, but you've been eating a bowl of lies for breakfast the whole time. It turns out that the delicious, multicolored Os that make up Froot Loops don't represent different fruit flavors. Kellogg's says that all of these delicious loops are flavored the same. If you fell into your cereal bowl after reading this, you are not alone. We have all been misled by these tantalizing lime green, orange, purple, yellow, and red loops as if they tasted of lime, orange, grape, lemon, cherry, and strawberry when in fact, they all have the same flavor. People at FoodBeast did some scientific blind testing and found the rumors to be true: Froot Loops all taste the same. They found that blind taste tests of "Trix" and "Fruity Pebbles" produced similar results.

44. When was the first espresso drunk in space?
A) In July 2010
B) In April 2012
C) In May 2015

In May 2015.
Italian astronaut Samantha Cristoforetti had the pleasure of tasting the first espresso brewed in space thanks to a pioneering coffee machine designed to operate in space. The aerospace engineers developed a new concept of coffee machine that is safe for astronauts and can function in microgravity conditions. This capsule-based coffee machine was created with the collaboration of Italian coffee maker "Lavazza," "Argotec" (an Italian engineering company that specializes in the design of aerospace systems), and the Italian Space Agency (ISA). The machine, which takes its name from the International Space Station, is called "ISSpresso" and can also create a variety of other hot drinks.

45. Are strawberries botanically seen as berries?
A) Yes
B) No
C) How should I know?

No, they're not.
Strawberries and raspberries are not actually berries in the botanical sense. They derive from a single flower with more than one ovary and are therefore an aggregate fruit. True berries are simple fruits that come from a flower with one ovary and typically have multiple seeds. Tomatoes fall into this group, as do pomegranates, kiwis, and, believe it or not, bananas. (Their seeds are so small it's easy to forget they're there.) So bananas are berries, and raspberries are not. Now you know.

46. How old are supermarket apples?
A) They are approximately 1 week old
B) They are around 1 month old
C) They can be up to 1 year old

They can be up to 1 year old.
In the USA, apples are harvested from August to November. Apples that will sell through December are regularly refrigerated. These huge warehouses are kept at 1-3 degrees Celsius (34-38 degrees Fahrenheit). Apples that will be sold later go to controlled atmosphere storage. They are stored at lower temperatures and oxygen levels. The oxygen level is reduced to 2 percent (the normal oxygen level is 21 percent). Sounds like they won't be as good anymore, but if handled and stored properly, the apples will taste just as when they went in. Apples lose some acidity when stored, but the nutritional content does not change significantly. This is why they can be sold for many months after harvesting.

47. What fruit glows blue under black light?
A) The kiwi
B) The banana
C) The orange

The banana.
The usual appearance of bananas is mainly due to carotenoids. These natural pigments appear yellow in normal light and blue under UV light (known to party guests as black light). However, green, unripe bananas do not fluoresce because the intensity of the luminescence correlates with the breakdown of the green pigment chlorophyll. Researchers in Austria were surprised to find that the intensity of the blue light peaks at the point where the fruit is perfect for eating. What an invention that would be: ripe bananas as the nightclub's new eatable glow sticks!

48. Have you ever eaten wasabi?
   A) Yes
   B) No
   C) Maybe

Probably you think yes, but maybe you have not, because most wasabi paste isn't real wasabi.
90 percent of the time that people eat "wasabi," they are actually eating dyed green horseradish. Now that we know we've been living our lives next to imposter wasabi, sharing our table and nasal passages with a fraud, let's get into how that could happen. Actual wasabi is extremely rare and extremely expensive; 2.2 pounds (1 kilogram) of wasabi can cost up to $250. One of the few places where wasabi grows naturally is in Japanese mountain streams. Wasabi plants require very special conditions in order to grow and thrive: constant flowing spring water, shade, rocky soil, and temperatures between 7 and 20 degrees Celsius (46 to 68 degrees Fahrenheit) year-round. So, wasabi is hard to grow, which makes it rare, which makes it expensive, which means you were probably eating green horseradish, and you didn't know until now.

49. What special beverage equipment is furnished in British battle tanks?

A) Juice press equipment

B) Beverage cooling equipment

C) Tea-making equipment

Tea-making equipment.

Few things are more British than tea, although it was originally a Portuguese tradition to brew South Asian leaves. The culture of tea drinking permeates British society–including the military. However, the culture of the tea break has been a major issue for the generals in charge of Britain's armored formations. Tank crew members had to stop and get out of their vehicle to have a brew, making it difficult to maintain an armored advance safely. The answer was the British Army boiling vessel: a built-in boiler for armored vehicles.

50. Why was the tomato feared in Europe in the late 1700s?

A) Because Europeans thought it looked dangerous

B) Because Europeans thought it was poisonous

C) Because Europeans thought it tasted bad

Because Europeans thought it was poisonous.

A nickname for the fruit was the "poison apple" because it was believed that aristocrats got sick and died after eating it. But the truth was that wealthy Europeans used pewter plates that were high in lead to serve the tomatoes. Because tomatoes have such a high acidity, when placed on this particular dish, the fruit would leach lead from the plate. This would lead to many deaths from lead poisoning. At the time, nobody made that connection between plate and poison, so the tomato was selected as the culprit.

51. Why was PEZ candy invented?

A) To help people quit smoking

B) To help people quit eating meat

C) To help people quit chewing gum

To help people quit smoking.

I think we all know PEZ, not for its especially good flavor but for the cool dispensers with their plastic head. PEZ, an abbreviation for "Pfefferminz," which is German and means peppermint, was invented in Austria in 1927 by Edward Haas. Haas developed a mint that he wanted to market as an alternative to smoking. In this way, Haas was way ahead of its time; cigarettes weren't considered bad back then. Although there's no evidence that peppermint is useful to stop smoking, the campaign proved to be quite successful in Austria. Probably because of the candy's sugar, which is now known as an effective drug addiction substitute, rather than the taste itself.

52. Which fast-food giant once made bubblegum-flavored broccoli?

A) McDonald's

B) Subway

C) Pizza Hut

McDonald's.

It sounds like one of Willy Wonka's rejected ideas, but this one is for real. Don Thompson, the chief executive of McDonald's, tried to create a way to get kids to eat healthier. This idea arose from the pressure of not having enough healthy options on the menu. Unfortunately, adding sweet bubblegum flavor to broccoli didn't make it more appetizing to children—they were more confused by it. Let's hope Willy Wonka will come up with a better idea!

53. What animal once put a man in the hospital because a shot bounced off it?
A) A turtle
B) An armadillo
C) A nautilus

An Armadillo.

A Texan man who tried to shoot an armadillo landed in the hospital after his bullet bounced off the animal and hit him in the face. The police said the man spotted the little animal "on his property" around 3:00 a.m. local time and decided to kill it. He went outside with his revolver and shot the armadillo three times. Its hard shell deflected at least one of the bullets, which bounced off and hit the man's jaw. That's karma!

54. How can flamingos balance on one leg while sleeping?
A) They have an excellent sense of balance
B) They have balance aids built into their bodies
C) They don't sleep with all parts of the brain at the same time

They have balance aids built into their bodies.

The fantastic balance flamingos have has something to do with their anatomy, especially a built-in "hold mechanism." The bird's skeleton seems to be the key. As in humans, flamingos have two main joints on their legs. The one you can see bending backward is not the knee. This is actually the bird's ankle. Its knee is hidden in the bird's features in the thicker part of its body. When the flamingo is ready to nod off, it will lift one leg and instinctively move its body so that its single foot is centered just below its carriage. Meanwhile, pulling up the other leg forces the knee on which the flamingo rests to bend. All of the joints essentially snap into place. Since the flamingo stays almost completely calm while sleeping, gravity does the rest and keeps the bird in place.

55. How do lobsters taste their food?

    A) With their nose
    B) With their legs
    C) With their antennas

With their legs.

The four small antennas on the front of the lobsters' heads are used to "smell" their food or chemicals in the water. Smell operates over distances, but taste requires physical contact. That's where the tiny sensory hairs on their legs come into play. They are used to "taste" their food. When the lobster smells food, it then crawls around until one of its legs brushes the food to get a taste of it.

56. How do sea cucumbers fight?

    A) They puff up to appear more dangerous
    B) They hide very fast
    C) They fight with their guts

They fight with their guts (literally).

The defenseless-looking sea cucumber has a secret weapon. When attacked, it spits sticky threads from its anus, tangling the hunter. Sea cucumbers can expel all of their intestines from their anus. This can confuse, repel, or feed predators. As extreme as this defense sounds, a cucumber can regenerate its internal organs quickly and without dying.

57. Can bees make colored honey?
A) Yes
B) No
C) It is not known

Yes, when they don't collect nectar from flowers.
Beekeepers in northeastern France found themselves in a difficult situation when their bees began producing honey in shades of blue and green from their hives. The honey was not allowed to be sold because it did not conform to French standards for honey production. Instead of collecting nectar from flowers, bees on site were feeding on leftover colored M&M candy shells that were being processed at a biogas plant about 2.5 miles (4 kilometers) away. The waste-processing plant discovered the problem at the same time as the beekeepers and quickly cleaned up all outdoor or uncovered containers where M&M waste had been stored. The candy residue is now stored in a covered shed.

58. How heavy is a blue whale's tongue?
A) It can weigh as much as an elephant
B) It can weigh as much as a horse
C) It can weigh as much as a pig

It can weigh as much as an elephant.
The blue whale dives to a depth of 330 feet (100 meters) to eat millions of krill a day and receives the award for the largest creature. These blue-gray giants are 80 to 100 feet (24 to 30 meters) long and weigh about 400,000 pounds (180,000 kilograms). This is equivalent to the weight of 135 cars. Its tongue alone weighs 5,400 pounds (2,400 kilograms), and a blue whale's

heart is about the size of a VW Beetle. Blue whales are quite large from birth and are considered to be the largest babies in the world. According to the World Wildlife Fund, a blue whale calf is about 26 feet (8 meters) long and weighs about 8,000 pounds (3,600 kilograms).

59. Who can hold their breath longer: sloths or dolphins?

A) Sloths

B) Dolphins

C) They can hold their breath for the same length of time

Sloths-they can hold their breath four times longer than dolphins.

Sloths are one of the most magical creatures in the world. They are adorable, love warm climates, laze around all day, and their furry bodies are home to hundreds of other organisms. But these lovable mammals have a lot more to offer than you might think. Sloths can swim three times faster in the water than they walk on land. And due to their ability to slow their heart rate to a third of its normal rate, they can hold their breath for 40 minutes, even underwater! On average, dolphins can hold their breath for a total of 8 to 10 minutes. They adjust their bodies as necessary to maximize their diving and catching fish time. Although Dolphins can slow the blood flow and heart rate of their circulatory system to conserve the energy and oxygen needed to stay underwater, sloths can hold their breath four times longer.

60. How big is the world's smallest wasp?

A) It is smaller than an ant

B) It is smaller than a grain of sand

C) It is smaller than an amoeba

It is smaller than an amoeba.

Fairies do exist and can be found in your garden. But you'd need a powerful microscope to see the dainty creatures. Fairy wasps are tiny parasitoid wasps with feather wings. Often, they are called fairy flies, which is a misnomer because they aren't actually a species of flies. Found in the United States, they belong to the Mymaridae family, which includes the smallest known insects in the world. Most species are less than 0.04 inches (1 millimeter) long—smaller than the average pinhead. And the smallest of all is a wingless male specimen of the fairy wasp at about 0.005 inches (0.13 millimeters). Many species of insects are sexually dimorphic, which means that males and females can look so different that they can be mistaken for different species. For the fairy wasp, the females are much larger than the record-breaking tiny males.

61. When do South American river turtles begin to communicate with one another?

A) When they are still in their eggs

B) When they are hatching

C) When they are in the ocean

When they are still in their eggs.

When it comes to saying their first "words," South American giant tortoises are amazingly precocious. Researchers discovered that the baby turtles begin to talk up to three days before hatching. Probably, the turtles communicate to coordinate hatching, which occurs 45 to 50 days after the eggs are laid. That offers security in numbers from predators. So when the turtles start to migrate, they'll call the other turtles and say "let's go, let's go, it's time."

62. Which animal washes its food before eating?

A) Wild boars
B) Elephants
C) Foxes

Wild boars.

Multiple animals submerge or manipulate their food in water prior to consumption. But not all of these animals actually have the intention of washing it. Some species of birds simply moisten their food to make it easier to swallow. Raccoons often roll it around in the water, but the behavior reflects their constant need to use their hands to sense the world and forage—not the urge to wash their food. To confirm that an animal really aims to remove dirt and sand from its food, researchers needed to see that it can distinguish between clean and dirty food and that it is deliberately moving dirty food to a water source. The discovery that some pigs wash their food came by accident. The communications officer at Basel Zoo in Switzerland noticed that wild boars put sandy apple halves in their mouths and carried them to the edge of a creek that ran through their habitat, put the pieces of fruit into the water, and manipulated them with their snouts before eating.

63. Is it okay to give your cat milk?

A) Yes, it's no problem
B) No, you shouldn't do it
C) Cat's love it, so why not?

No, you shouldn't do it.

In children's stories, cats and milk always seem made for each other. Who hasn't seen adorable illustrations of a kitten licking a saucer of cream? Most cats do love a little milk, but milk doesn't always return that affection. The main culprit is lactose which many cats have trouble digesting. Just like humans, cats can be lactose intolerant. In order to digest lactose, a milk sugar, the human and feline digestive systems must contain the enzyme lactase. At birth, we have plenty of this enzyme in our bodies, and it helps us live off our mother's milk. But as we grow up, it's normal for humans and cats to produce less lactase. Less lactase means less ability to digest lactose. The result: diarrhea or an upset stomach.

64. How many hearts does an octopus have?
A) 1
B) 2
C) 3

Octopuses have 3 hearts.
1 pumps blood around the body, and the other 2 pump blood into the gills. The reason for this impressive heart hardware is likely due to the unusual composition of their blood. In contrast to vertebrates, which have iron-rich hemoglobin in red blood cells, octopuses have copper-rich hemocyanin dissolved right in their blood (funny side note: this makes their blood blue!). Because hemocyanin is less effective as an oxygen transporter, the three hearts are needed to compensate for this by pumping blood around the body at higher pressures.

65. Which animals have the most neck bones?
A) Sloths and manatees
B) Giraffes and lamas
C) Ostriches and flamingos

Sloths and manatees.
Really? Is it not the giraffe? Nope. As a rule, all mammals have the same number of vertebrae in their neck, regardless of whether they are a giraffe, mouse, elephant, or human. But both sloths and

manatees are exceptions to this rule, with ten vertebrae instead of seven. It is believed that it's their slow lifestyle and low metabolic rate that have allowed evolution to change their neck lengths.

66. How high could a bumblebee fly?

A) Higher than the highest roller coaster

B) Higher than the highest building in the world

C) Higher than Mount Everest

Higher than Mount Everest.

Scientists have found that alpine bumblebees have the ability to fly at elevations greater than Mount Everest, but they cannot survive the freezing conditions at its peak. Researchers at the University of California simulated the conditions of low oxygen and air density at such high elevations to determine the limits of the bumblebee's flight capacity and found that the bees would be able to stay afloat at remarkably inhospitable elevations.

67. Which animal was used by Ancient Egyptians to ease toothaches?

A) The mouse

B) The cat

C) The dog

The mouse.

The ancient Egyptians put a dead mouse in their mouth in the hope that it would relieve toothache. In some cases, mashed mice were mixed with other ingredients, and the resulting poultice was applied to the painful area. The Egyptians weren't the only ones engaged in mouse cures. In Elizabethan England, one remedy for warts was to cut a mouse in half and apply it to the affected area. Mice were also used to treat whooping cough, measles, smallpox, and bed-wetting. To top it all off, the Elizabethans also ate mice–fried or baked in cakes. Eww!

68. Why can't cows really bite you?
A) Because they don't have front teeth
B) Because they don't have lower front teeth
C) Because they don't have upper front teeth

Because they don't have upper front teeth.
Cows are unique in that they have fewer teeth than other animals. In the front of the mouth, they have teeth only on the bottom jaw. Instead of the upper teeth, there is a hard leather pad. Because of this unique oral anatomy, a cow reaches for a tuft of grass with its tongue and "bites" it off. But in the back of the mouth, teeth are located on the upper and lower jaw, which they use for chewing the grass.

69. Which animal lay 56,000 eggs at a time?
A) The turtle
B) The octopus
C) The crocodile

The octopus.
A pregnant squid carries the eggs in her body for 4 to 5 months. One day, when the water temperature is right, she begins to expel her eggs into the water, one by one. She produces about 56,000 individual eggs, which takes about a month. Later, after some more months of guarding the eggs, the female octopus dies when their babies descend into the ocean. Out of these 56,000 eggs, sadly, only about two of them make it to adulthood.

70. How long are giraffe tongues?
A) Up to 16 inches (40 centimeters)
B) Up to 18 inches (45 centimeters)
C) Up to 20 inches (50 centimeters)

They are up to 20 inches (50 centimeters) long.

Much like their necks, giraffe tongues are exceptionally long–usually between 18 and 20 inches (45 to 50 centimeters) long. They're also prehensile, which means that giraffes have fine-tuned muscular control over them. This allows them to grab leaves and shoots and pull them into their mouths. The dark purple color of the tongue is supposed to prevent sunburn. This may sound strange at first, but it makes sense considering that giraffes spend most of their day sticking their tongues out to retrieve grass shoots and leaves.

71. How many calories do blue whales eat in one mouthful?
A) One quarter million calories
B) Half a million calories
C) One million calories

Half a million calories.

The average person consumes 2,000 calories a day. Doesn't sound like a lot compared to the blue whale, eh? Scientists in Canada estimated that a blue whale can eat 480 million calories of food in a single dive (which lasts about 10 to 20 minutes). In one day, these whales consume around 12,500 pounds of food to fuel their body! 8 months a year feeding occurs, and then the whales live on their blubber reserves for the other 4 months.

Humorous History

72. What was the tiny pocket in jeans designed for?
A) To look high-end
B) To hide keys
C) To store pocket watches

To store pocket watches.
Those little pockets are far too small to be useful. But in the olden days, they were designed to hold a pocket watch. They are not usually found on suit pants because suit jackets already have pockets for watches. These days, people tend to check the time on their cell phones or watches, so pretty much no one carries around a pocket watch. However, the small pockets are kept in jeans today to maintain the integrity of the original design.

73. How long did the shortest war in history last?
A) 18 minutes
B) 28 minutes
C) 38 minutes

It lasted 38 minutes.
On August 27th, 1896, five Royal Navy ships began bombing the Royal Palace and Harem in Zanzibar. 38 minutes later, the bombardment stopped as the white flag of surrender was raised over the remains of the palace. Over 500 defenders died compared to one injured British Marine. This ended what is known as the "shortest war in history." The immediate cause of the war was the death of the Sultan of Zanzibar, Hamad bin Thuwaini, on August 25th. His nephew took power but was seen by the British as

far too independent. In the best tradition of gunboat diplomacy, an ultimatum was issued, giving Khalid an hour to surrender and leave the palace. When the ultimatum expired, the bombardment began. The nephew was quickly and secretly shipped out of the country. Order was restored, and the preferred ruler, Hamud bin Muhammed, was installed as Sultan of Zanzibar, where he ruled with British support until his death in 1902.

74. When was the first female elected to Congress in the United States?
A) In 1916
B) In 1936
C) In 1956

In 1916, even before women had the right to vote nationally. Jeannette Rankin of Montana was the first woman elected to Congress. Rankin had campaigned as a progressive in 1916, pledging to work for a change in constitutional women's suffrage and to emphasize social welfare issues. She was a committed pacifist for a long time and against US involvement in the European war that had been raging for two years.

In 1917, she arrived at the Capitol to be sworn in with the other members of the 65th Congress (1917-1919). When her name was mentioned, the house cheered and rose so that she had to rise and bow twice, which she did in complete self-possession.

75. What did Americans use before toilet paper?
A) Leather
B) Corn cobs
C) Their clothes

Corn cobs.

Anyone who's gone camping will know that a handful of dry leaves comes in handy when there's no toilet paper around. Modern toilet paper wasn't available in the United States until the mid-19th century. Before it was made in the ubiquitous four-and-a-half-inch rolls we all know and love, toilet paper came in bundles of flat sheets about the size of a box of today's facial tissues. But before that time, native Americans used twigs, dry grass, small stones, and even oyster or clamshells. In rural farming communities, handfuls of straw were often used, but one of the most popular means of cleaning was dried corn cobs. They were plentiful and very efficient at cleaning—they could be drawn in one direction or rotated around an axis. They were also softer in sensitive areas than you might think. Even after toilet paper became available, some people in western states preferred corn cobs when using the outhouse.

76. When does the first urine-based pregnancy test date back to?

A) It dates back to 450 BC.

B) It dates back to 850 BC.

C) It dates back to 1,350 BC.

It dates back to 1,350 BC.

One of the earliest written records of a urine-based pregnancy test is found in an ancient Egyptian document. One papyrus described a test in which a pregnant woman could urinate on wheat and barley seeds for several days: If the barley grows, it means she'll have a male child; if the wheat grows, a female one. And if neither grows, she won't bear at all. Tests of this theory in 1963 found that 70 percent of the time, the urine of pregnant women promoted growth, while the urine of non-pregnant women and men did not. Scientists have identified this as possibly the first test to detect a unique substance in the urine of pregnant women and have speculated that elevated levels of estrogen in the urine of pregnant women may have been the key to success.

77. Why were roller coasters invented?

A) To make people more content

B) To distract people from immoral behavior

C) To show off the latest inventions

To distract people from immoral behavior.

Riding roller coasters is one of the most popular pastimes in the world. People sometimes wait for hours to ride the newest thrill ride or an old classic. There are many reasons why we enjoy riding roller coasters: People love the speed, the apparent danger, and like a small child riding a wagon a little too fast on a winding side path, we like to be scared. Oddly enough, none of these things was the main reason behind the invention of the roller coaster. What motivated the inventor of the roller coaster at the end of the 19th century was immorality. Believing that America had both created and rushed into a cave of iniquity, LaMarcus Adna Thompson was looking for a pastime that would pull Americans away from the tavernas, game and dance halls, and brothels. Thompson was inspired by people riding an old mining railway for fun and built his own "Switchback Railway." In three weeks, Thompson was making about $600 a day—that's the equivalent of $15,000 a day today! It didn't take long until others started to develop their own switchback railways.

78. How long did the first commercial passenger flight last?

A) 13 minutes

B) 23 minutes

C) 33 minutes

It lasted only 23 minutes.

In 1914, on January 1st, the world's first scheduled airline took off between St. Petersburg and Tampa, Florida. The St. Petersburg-Tampa Airboat Line was short-lived, but it paved the way for today's daily transcontinental flights. Abram C. Pheil, former mayor of St. Petersburg, was the first paying passenger. The 21-mile (34-kilometer) flight across the bay to Tampa took 23 minutes. Pheil paid $400 (more than $8,500 in today's dollars) but considering the alternative transport options, it may have been worth it. A trip between the two cities on opposite sides of Tampa Bay took up to 12 hours by train. The drive through the bay by car took about 20 hours.

79. Where did baseball umpires use to be during a game?
A) They used to be sitting in a rocking chair
B) They used to be sitting in a spectator seat
C) They used to be sitting on the ground

They used to be sitting in a rocking chair.
Baseball has been around for over one hundred years, and in the early days, umpires would officiate games reclining in a rocking chair positioned 20 feet behind home plate. Imagine seeing this in today's game on national television! In 1878, the National League also declared that home teams had to pay umpires $5 per game.

80. What was the biggest empire in history?
A) The Roman Empire
B) The Greek Empire
C) The British Empire

The British Empire.
The British Empire began with colonies and trading posts overseas and ended up including dominions, protectorates, and mandates. It covered 13.01 million square miles (33.6 million square kilometers) of land—more than 22 percent of the Earth's landmass. In 1938, the empire had 458 million people—more than 20 percent

of the world's population. The financial burden of World War I was the beginning of the end for the British Empire. Finally, Japan's occupation of its territories in World War II and the loss of India in 1947 ended the glorious days of the British Empire.

81. What did paint used to be stored in?

A) In pig bladders

B) In horse stomaches

C) In cow intestines

In pig bladders.

John G. Rand, a brilliant but little-known American portrait painter, struggled to keep his oil paints from drying out before he could use them. At that time (1841), a pig's bladder sealed with string was the best paint storage device. The artist poked the bladder with a pencil to extract the paint. But there was no way to completely seal the hole afterward, and the bladders did not transport well and often burst. But Ran came up with a revolutionary invention: the paint tube. This foldable pewter tube, sealed with a screw cap, made the paint last a long time, did not leak, and could be opened and closed again and again.

82. When was the first official aquarium opened?

A) In 1853

B) In 1913

C) In 1963

In 1853.

The earliest documented aquarists were the Sumerians, who kept freshwater fish in man-made ponds at least 4,500 years ago, and records of fish keeping also date from ancient Egypt. However, only in 1853, the Zoological Society of London opened the first modern public aquarium, displaying over 300 marine species in closed tanks called the "Fish House." The term aquarium (which comes from classical Latin: a watering place for cattle) was coined by the British naturalist Philip Henry Gosse and shortly thereafter adopted and popularized by the London Zoo. 8 years later, in 1938, the first oceanarium (large saltwater aquarium), Marineland, opened in Florida.

83. Who invented glitter?

A) A New Jersey cattle rancher

B) A New Jersey beekeeper

C) A New Jersey teacher

A New Jersey cattle rancher.

You might not have expected it, but glitter has actually been used as a decoration since prehistoric times. Cave paintings were discovered with mica flakes mixed in to give them a shimmering appearance. The word "glitter" itself comes from the Old Norse word "glitra" and means "shine," but modern glitter as we know it today was not invented until 1934. The inventor, Henry Ruschmann, tried to figure out a way to dispose of plastic. He shredded it and accidentally fabricated glitter.

Talking about glitter and shine... Even if it isn't 5 shining stars, I'd really appreciate it if you left a review for this book (nice transition eh?). So if you're enjoying this book or you're just a nice person that likes to support others, click this link or scan the QR Code below:

Amazon.com/review/create-review?&asin=B09N3WYLB4

Thanks a lot! Now onto the next chapter where we talk about incredible human accomplishments - greater ones than convincing you to write a quick review on Amazon (let me know if it worked).

Famous and Not-So-Famous People

84. Who is the man with the world's deepest voice?
A) Tim Thunders
B) Tim Hurricane
C) Tim Storms

Tim Storms.

The hearing range of most mammals is wider than the range of frequencies they can produce with their voices. For example, the human ear can hear frequencies up to 20 kHz, but we cannot scream higher than approximately 3 kHz. The lower end of our listening range is around 20 Hz. This is still just below the lowest notes most of us normally make, which is around 85 Hz. US singer Tim Storms, however, can sing a note at 0.189 Hz, or eight octaves below the lowest G note on the piano. Crazy!

85. What did Michelangelo write on the ceiling of the Sistine Chapel?
A) A poem about how he didn't like painting the chapel
B) A poem about how he enjoyed painting the chapel
C) A poem about how grateful he was for painting the chapel

A poem about how he didn't like painting the chapel.

Michelangelo, one of the best-known artists in history, didn't always enjoy his (art) work. As a gifted poet, sculptor and painter, he wrote energetically about desperation and described with relish the unpleasant side of his work on the famous ceiling. The poem conveys that the Italian artist knew well enough that he and his work were great but that he enjoyed violently lamenting his discomfort, pain, and inadequacy for the job. "My painting is dead" or "I am not at the right place–I'm not a painter" are parts of the poem that demonstrate his despair due to the hard time working on this challenging project.

86. Who scored the winning goal in the first World Cup?

A) The one-legged Héctor Castro

B) The one-armed Héctor Castro

C) The one-footed Héctor Castro

The one-armed Héctor Castro.

Although today's highly professional world of football may at first glance seem like a zone of no disability, when we look back on the first World Cup tournament in 1930, Héctor Castro, a one-armed man, played an extremely important role. In the 89th minute, he scored the sixth and final goal of Uruguay's 4-2 win in the 1930 playoff. Castro had lost half an arm in an accident with an electric saw thirteen years earlier and, despite this amputated limb, won Olympic gold and scored the first and, above all, last goal in Uruguay.

87. Does Queen Elizabeth II have a secret double?

A) Yes

B) No

C) We don't know, it's a secret

Not, but she has a "stand-in" for rehearsals.

Technically, the Queen does not have a body double. There is currently no person attending engagements in place of the queen. However, Ella Slack has played an important behind-the-scenes role as a "stand-in" for the Queen over the past three decades. Ella Slack insists that she is not a lookalike. "I don't look like the Queen–but I have the same stature and size," she explains. Ms. Slack's job is to help promoters, stage managers, and production staff figure out exactly how the Queen will fit into important events.

It all started when she was at the BBC when the Queen stood on the Cenotaph, and there was sunshine in her eyes. Since the stage managers were all six-foot-tall men, Ms. Slack stood in the Queen's place so they could adjust the lighting. This first substitute role led to other assignments, including driving the Queen's royal carriage and attending the rehearsal for the opening of Parliament. Of course, since Mrs. Slack is not the Queen, she still has to follow certain protocols. She is never allowed to sit on the throne in the House of Lords but must lurk above it. This is a very strict rule. However, Ms. Slack is allowed to give the iconic royal wave in the Queen's carriage. And who doesn't want to do that?!

88. Which former US President was shot right after giving away his good-luck charm?
A) Abraham Lincoln
B) William McKinley
C) Theodore Roosevelt

William McKinley.

William McKinley is one of the few presidents that have been assassinated, but his assassination has a very special twist. McKinley had worn a lucky red carnation on his lapel for years, but one day he decided to give it to a little girl at the Pan American Exhibition in Buffalo, New York. Moments later, he was shot, which apparently shows that lucky charms are very real, at least in his case.

89. Who tries to fix the internet?

A) Its creator
B) Its shareholders
C) Nobody

Its creator, Tim Berners-Lee.

The inventor of the World Wide Web officially launched his plan to "fix" the Internet. The World Wide Web Foundation, a nonprofit campaign group, founded by Berners-Lee, has won the support of technology giants Facebook, Google, and Microsoft for what is known as the "Contract for the Web" program. The treaty calls on companies to respect consumer privacy and urges governments to ensure that everyone has access to the internet. "Never before has the web's power for good been more under threat," said Adrian Lovett, CEO of the World Wide Web Foundation. He added that the rise of hateful content and fake news spread online means that something has to change. They are planning to launch the world's first global action plan to protect the Internet as a driving force. It will bring together businesses, governments, and citizens from around the world to get things back on track.

90. What do Mahatma Gandhi, Eleanor Roosevelt, and Adolf Hitler have in common?

A) They have all been Nobel Peace Prize nominees
B) They have all been assassinated
C) They have all been born less than 150 years ago

They have all been Nobel Peace Prize nominees.

Yes, Adolf Hitler, the genocidal mastermind of the Shoah, was nominated to the Nobel Committee in 1939, just three months before he led Germany to invade Poland and start World War II. The recommendation came from a Social Democratic member of the Swedish Parliament, Erik Gottfrid Christian Brandt. (Members of national assemblies are among the many people who can nominate candidates for the Peace Prize.) In his letter to the committee, he calls the Führer "a God-given fighter for peace" and "the Prince of Peace on Earth." He calls *Mein Kampf* "the best and most popular piece of literature in the world" and is confident that the dictator can "pacify Europe and possibly the whole world." Sound like sarcasm? It definitely was. Brandt was an anti-fascist and had described the letter as ironic. Later in 1939, after the war broke out, he wrote that he had wanted to use the letter's sarcasm to "nail Hitler to the wall of shame" as enemy number one of world peace. Angered by the prestigious award, which had been given to his critic Carl von Ossietzky in 1935, Hitler had banned all Germans from accepting the prize.

91. Why is the British royal family named Windsor?
A) They're named after the fashion brand Windsor
B) They're named after the House of Windsor
C) They're named after the town of Windsor

They're named after the House of Windsor, which was founded in 1917.

Before 1917, the British royal family members did not bear a surname but only the name of the house or dynasty to which they belonged. Kings and princes were historically known by the names of the countries over which they and their families ruled. Therefore, royal family members only signed their first names (a tradition in the UK that continues to this day). There was a radical change in 1917 when George V specifically adopted Windsor, not only as the name of the house or dynasty but also as his family's family name. With this proclamation, he replaced the historic name of Saxe-Coburg-Gotha, and Windsor still remains the family name of today's royal family.

The President of the United States.

The President of the United States receives approximately 60 to 80,000 letters a week. This is on top of the 100,000 emails and thousands of phone calls that come in every day. All correspondence sent to the President is processed, and due to the amount of mail sent to the White House, it is difficult for the President to receive personal mail. A letter sent to the White House by a personal friend or family member of the President would go through all necessary reviews before potentially being forwarded to staff who could, at best, forward the letter to a Secretary of the President. It is unlikely that the President will ever see a letter through these channels. But presidents have personal friends as well; they have family members who want to mail Christmas cards, they have bill collectors, and they need mail from outside the White House bubble. That's why the US Postal Service sets a secret personal zip code for the President's use. The President's personal zip code is shared with people he wishes to receive mail from during his time at the White House—a sort of VIP list for letters. If the secret zip code is somehow leaked, the postal service will issue a new one.

93. Who invented ice pops?

A) An 11-year-old entrepreneur

B) A 41-year-old entrepreneur

C) A 71-year-old entrepreneur

An 11-year-old entrepreneur.

Back in 1905, a kid from the San Francisco Bay Area named Frank Epperson accidentally invented the summer snack. He had mixed some sugary soda powder with water and left it outside overnight. It was a cold night, and the mixture froze. In the morning, Epperson gobbled up the icy concoction and licked it off the wooden stirrer. He called it "Epsicle," a word made up of icicles and his name, and began selling the treat in his neighborhood. In 1923, Epperson decided to expand sales beyond his neighborhood. He began selling the treat at Neptune Beach, a nearby amusement park. Neptune prospered in the days before the Depression, and consumers eagerly consumed Epsicles. Spurred by this success, Epperson applied for a patent in 1924 for his "frozen confection of attractive appearance which can be conveniently eaten without contamination by touching with the hand and without the necessity of a plate, spoon, fork or other utensils."

94. How much was Neil Armstrong's hair illegally sold for?

A) It was sold for $3,000
B) It was sold for $30,000
C) It was sold for $300,000

It was sold for $3,000.

Apollo moon mission astronaut Neil Armstrong has threatened to sue a barbershop owner who sold the space traveler's hair for $3,000. The buyer, John Reznikoff, said that he would not return the locks but would donate the purchase price to charity. He is a collector listed by the Guinness World Records as the largest collection of hair by historical celebrities. His collection, which is insured for $1 million, includes hair from Abraham Lincoln, Marilyn Monroe, Albert Einstein, and Napoleon. The barber, Marx Sizemore, received a letter from the former astronaut's attorney claiming the sale violated an Ohio law designed to protect the rights of famous people. The letter threatens legal action if Sizemore doesn't return the hair or doesn't use his winnings for charity and asks him to pay Armstrong's legal expenses. But Sizemore said he won't pay and has already spent most of the $3,000 on bills. Uff!

95. What grade did Martin Luther King Jr. get in public speaking at seminary school?

A) He got an A

B) He got a B

C) He got a C

He got a C.

Although King is undoubtedly an example of the greatest speakers of the English language of the 20th century, he once showed little academic promise in this department. It is hard to believe that the man who would become the most prolific public speaker of our time, who would deliver the "I Have A Dream speech," could come close to failing a public speaking course. But in his first year of seminary school in Chester, Pennsylvania, one of King's professors gave him a C in the public speaking course! He definitely practiced and improved because, in his third and final year, King was valedictorian with straight A's.

96. Who stated that pigeon poop was their property?

A) Queen Margrethe II of Denmark

B) King George I of England

C) King Carl XVI Gustav of Sweden

King George I of England.

Although pigeon poo is seen as a major problem for property owners in the 21st century, it was considered an invaluable resource in Europe in the 16th, 17th, and 18th centuries. Pigeon poop was a highly valued fertilizer and was thought to be far more effective than farmyard manure. In fact, it was so valued that armed guards were stationed at the entrances to dovecotes (pigeon houses) to stop thieves from stealing them. Not only that, but in England in the 16th century, pigeon poo was the only known source of saltpeter, an essential component of gunpowder, so King George I confirmed that the droppings were owned by the Crown.

97. Who won the 2015 French-language Scrabble World Championship?

A) A native New Zealander who speaks French

B) A native New Zealander who doesn't speak French

C) A native New Zealander who is blind

A native New Zealander who doesn't speak French.
Nigel Richards' Scrabble career went from great to astounding the week after winning the French-speaking Scrabble World Championships. The native New Zealander had already won several English language titles, and his new victory followed weeks of studying a French dictionary. How was he able to do that? Basically, he looked at word lists and dictionary pages, conjured up the picture of what he's seen, and that's enough for him to remember it. French Scrabble has 386,000 words. That's a lot—way more than North American Scrabble, which has 187,000 words. But the game isn't just about remembering words, it's a game of strategy and spatial relationships on the board, but Nigel seems to master it all.

98. Which American President was a licensed bartender?

A) Abraham Lincoln

B) Theodore Roosevelt

C) John F. Kennedy

Abraham Lincoln.
Lincoln was a co-owner of "Berry and Lincoln," a drinking

establishment that he founded with his friend William F. Berry. It was located in New Salem, Illinois, where he lived from 1831 to 1837. Stores could sell alcohol in quantities greater than 1 pint (half a liter) for off-premises consumption, but it was illegal to sell individual drinks to consume at the store without a license. In March 1833, Berry and Lincoln obtained a tavern license for $7 so they could serve half-pints (24 centiliters) of French brandy for 25 cents and other liquors for ridiculous prices. Unfortunately (or maybe fortunately), Lincoln's foray into the world of booze was short-lived. Berry was apparently an alcoholic and took advantage of the new license to drink while working in the store, which is why they went into debt.

99. Which famous musician did not know how to multiply?

A) Ludwig van Beethoven
B) Wolfgang Amadeus Mozart
C) Johann Sebastian Bach

Ludwig van Beethoven.

Beethoven was a virtuoso pianist from a young age and toured Europe with great success before becoming deaf in his late twenties/early thirties. Despite this seemingly debilitating illness, Beethoven continued to compose some of the greatest works of the Classical and Romantic periods and embodied the epitome of the human spirit of perseverance. Although being one of the most brilliant brains in the world, he wasn't able to multiply or divide. Because Beethoven had left school at the age of eleven to help with the household income, he never learned. For example, if he had to multiply "30 x 52," he would lay out thirty 52 times and add them up.

100. How much did Percy Spencer, the inventor of the microwave, receive for his discovery?
A) $2
B) $200
C) $2,000

Only $2.

When the product hit the market in 1947, weighing 750 pounds and costing over $2,000, it was a flop. Spencer had over 300 patents but received only $2 as a bonus for his invention. In 1999, he was immortalized for his invention and was inducted into the National Inventors Hall of Fame, which honors other famous inventors such as Thomas Edison and the Wright Brothers.

101. Which American president owned a pet hyena?
A) Abraham Lincoln
B) Benjamin Harrison
C) Theodore Roosevelt

Theodore Roosevelt.

Theodore Roosevelt and his family had many pets during their lifetime and were known to be great animal lovers. When the world learned of the family's love for animals, diplomatic leaders began sending exotic animals as gifts. Among them was a hyena named Bill. Bill was a gift to President Roosevelt from Emperor Menelik II of Ethiopia. Some sources say that Roosevelt loved this particular hyena and even allowed him to live in the White House for a while. In the end, Bill was sent to the National Zoo along with Joe the Lion to live out the remainder of their days.

102. What did the poet T.S. Eliot always wear on his face?

A) Mascara

B) Eyeliner

C) Green makeup

Green makeup.

After T. S. Eliot wrote The Waste Land, he started wearing green-tinted face powder. No one knew why he was doing it, but there were several rumors. The English art critic Clive Bell, for example, said he thought Eliot powdered his face to look "interesting and cadaverous." His biographer Peter Ackroyd agreed: Wearing face powder made Eliot feel more modern, more interesting, more of a poet than a bank clerk.

103. Who designed the current American flag?

A) An 11-year-old student

B) A 17-year-old student

C) A 23-year-old student

A 17-year-old student named Robert Heft.

Heft's teacher challenged his students to design a new 50-star flag after Hawaii and Alaska joined the Union. Robert designed it with 5 rows of six stars and 4 rows of five stars and spent 12.5 hours sewing the flag. His teacher thought the design was unoriginal and graded it a B but offered to give him an A if the design was nationally recognized. Heft accepted the challenge and contacted the White House. Two years later, his school project was selected as the national flag.

7 Bonus Questions

> **1.** Mickey, Minnie, Donald Duck, Pinocchio, and other Disney characters all have one accessory in common: gloves. Do you know why?

To keep the animation easier.
Animation is an exhausting process. It takes time and extreme precision to create the characters we now know. Animators wanted to make their job easier and faster with a few techniques and hacks. One of these strategies was to use rounded edges instead of angles. This also meant simplifying functions like hands to speed up the animation process.

> **2.** What is the first number that contains the letter A?

Just keep counting, you'll find out.
I'm kidding, this would take too long... the answer is one thousand. Although A is second in the number of appearances in the Concise Oxford English Dictionary, it is nowhere to be found in the English spellings of the first 999 numbers. Every other vowel appears (including Y). But A is not the last letter that appears when counting. The first number that contains a Q is one quadrillion, and for P it's one septillion!

3. You may already be familiar with Queen Elizabeth II's obsession with corgis and horses, or the fact that she has the right to claim ownership of any unmarked mute swan swimming in open waters. But do you also know where her cows sleep?

They sleep on waterbeds.
As expected, Queen Elizabeth's 165 dairy cows are treated royally. Not only do they wander around and graze in huge green pastures, but they can also rub up against an automatic cow brush that removes dirt and relieves stress. Meanwhile, robots milk the cows and clean the floors, which means the cattle can come in in their own time rather than being left to the whims of a human milk farmer. But perhaps the greatest luxury the cattle enjoy is the water beds. The cows lie down on large pillows of water to sleep, but they also like to hang out on them during the day. As the cow lies down, the water pushes below where the cow lies, and they end up floating. Sounds positively dreamy! We may have to revisit the 70s and get our own waterbeds.

4. What bizarre injury did Brad Pitt sustain on the set of Troy?

Ironically, an Achilles tendon injury.
Pitt made an effort to get fit for the character of Achilles. As he admitted in an interview prior to the film's release, he worked hard for six months to get in shape. He ate 4 high-protein meals a day, exercised to build a lot of strength, and also kept carbohydrates to a minimum. However, all of his training couldn't stop him from inflicting an injury to his Achilles tendon while filming. The injury suspended filming for several weeks while Pitt recovered enough to resume production. While the film didn't get the best of reviews when it was released, there was no doubt that Pitt certainly looked like Achilles—injured foot and everything.

5. How much was the Terminator script sold for?

For $1.
James Cameron was not considered trustworthy as a director because of the failure of Piranha II (his previous movie). Nobody wanted him to direct the film, but he received many offers for the script from studios that were not interested in hiring him to direct. Although some of the offers involved large sums of money, he turned them all down. According to Cameron, the idea for the script came to him in a dream, and he was very attached to it. Eventually, he struck a deal with his co-writer, Hurd. Cameron would sell her full rights to the script for a dollar, on the condition that he could direct the film. Hurd agreed to Cameron's deal, and while Cameron got his wish to be the director of The Terminator, the post-release success probably made him completely regret his decision.

6. Is it possible to hum while holding your nose?

I bet you just tried it out, but no, it's not.
Why is this so? Because when you hum, you actually exhale. So when both your mouth and nose are closed, the air cannot escape. Although you can hum for a second or two, you will be forced to open your mouth and catch your breath.

7. Why does NASA use countdowns for the rocket launch?

Because of the science fiction pioneer Fritz Lang.
With countdown clocks, technicians and astronauts can synchronize their movements during a rocket launch sequence

from T-minus 43 hours until final ignition. However, their appeal goes way beyond practicality. The clock also serves as the visual version of a whistling teakettle, so viewers can ramp up their excitement as launch time draws nearer. When those last seconds pass before the start, it is dramatic, emotional–even cinematic. Which makes sense given the fact that the countdown clock for the rocket launch was not invented by meticulous engineers but by the filmmaker Fritz Lang. Although some previous novels and films used count-ups, the "Die Frau im Mond" movie was the first time the rocket met the countdown. Since then, they have been inseparable.

Conclusion

We are already at the end of our adventure, and I hope you enjoyed this fun trivia quiz. Probably, you won't remember most of the facts but don't let this stop you from staying curious and learning more.

That being said, how did you like the book? Let me know by leaving a review. You can click right here or scan the code below. It only takes 30 seconds, and this would really help me out. I'm sending greetings to you in advance!

Amazon.com/review/create-review?&asin=B09N3WYLB4

P.S. Here's another entertaining trivia book I wrote that you might enjoy. Check it out!

https://www.amazon.com/dp/B096TTR9VX

Impress your friends with some SURPRISING FACTS!

Thank you so much, I wish you only the best!

Sources

6 Famous Discontinued and Uncommon U.S. Currency Denominations. (2020, September 9). Investopedia. https://www.investopedia.com/6-famous-discontinued-and-uncommon-u-s-currency-denominations-4773302#:%7E:-text=The%20Bureau%20of%20Engraving%20and%20Printing%20created%20them%20during%20the,%24100%2C000%20bills%20were%20ever%20printed.

The 10 Greatest Empires In The History Of The World. (2017, May 12). Business Insider. https://www.businessinsider.com/the-10-greatest-empires-in-history-2011-9?r=US&IR=T#1-the-british-empire-was-the-largest-empire-the-world-has-ever-seen-10

11 Things You Might Not Know About Giraffes. (2020, November 11). Treehugger. https://www.treehugger.com/giraffe-facts-5072826#:%7E:text=Much%20like%20their%20necks%2C%20giraffe,and%20shoots%20into%20their%20mouths

A. (2020a, September 3). *Brad Pitt's on-set injury on "Troy" is a strange tribute to his character Achilles.* FR24 News. https://www.fr24news.com/a/2020/09/brad-pitts-on-set-injury-on-troy-is-a-strange-tribute-to-his-character-achilles.html

Aimee, A. (2014, November 14). *Why McDonald's created bubble gum-flavored broccoli.* CBS News. https://www.cbsnews.com/news/why-mcdonalds-created-bubble-gum-flavored-broccoli/

Animal Facts - Lobsters. (n.d.). Vegan Peace. https://www.veganpeace.com/animal_facts/Lobsters.htm#:%7E:text=The%20four%20small%20antennae%20on,and%20to%20watch%20for%20enemies

Baby giant South American river turtles talk to each other from inside eggs. (2014, August 29). CBC. https://www.cbc.ca/news/science/baby-giant-south-american-river-turtles-talk-to-each-other-from-inside-eggs-1.2747542

Barrabi, T. (2020, June 18). *Rare Nike "waffle iron" shoes could fetch $150K at auction.* Fox Business. https://www.foxbusiness.com/sports/nike-waffle-iron-shoes-bill-bowerman-auction

Bartender-In-Chief: Abraham Lincoln Owned A Tavern. (2013, February 12). The Chicagoist. https://chicagoist.com/2013/02/12/abraham_lincoln_bartender.php#:%7E:text=Back%20before%20he%20was%20President%2C%20Abraham%20Lincoln%20was%20a%20lawyer.&tex-

t=But%20Lincoln%20was%20the%20only,lived%20from%201831%20 to%201837.+https://www.wannafactph.com/2020/07/pigeon-poop-crown.html

Baseball umpires used to sit in rocking chairs. (n.d.). NTKF. https://www.need-toknowfacts.com/sports/baseball-umpires-used-to-sit-in-rocking-chairs

Bates, M. (2021, May 3). *Picky Pigs Take Washing Certain Foods Seriously.* Animals. https://www.nationalgeographic.com/animals/article/151023-wild-boar-pigs-wash-food-animals-behavior-science#:%7E:text=Cleaning%20 Up,and%20primates%20all%20do%20so.

BBC - Ouch! (disability) - Fact - Ouch Q&A: HÃ©ctor Castro 1930s disabled football star. (2007, June 7). BBC. https://www.bbc.co.uk/ouch/fact/ q_a_h_ctor_castro_1930s_disabled_football_star.shtml

BBC News. (2015, September 23). *Scots "have 421 words" for snow.* https:// www.bbc.com/news/uk-scotland-34323967#:%7E:text=Scotland%20 has%20more%20than%20400,%22%20(a%20large%20snowflake).

Beach, J. (2019, April 9). *10 crazy traffic laws you didn't know you were breaking as a cyclist.* BikeRadar. https://www.bikeradar.com/featu-res/10-crazy-traffic-laws-you-didnt-know-you-were-breaking-as-a-cyc-list/#:%7E:text=5.,riding%20in%20Galesburg%2C%20Illinois%2C%20 USA&text=It's%20true%2C%20we've%20looked,fancy%20riding%20 on%20any%20street.%E2%80%9D

Beefalo. (n.d.). American Beefalo Association. http://americanbeefaloassociation. com/benefits

Booth, J. (2019, January 25). *McDonald's Sells A McSpaghetti Dinner Meal, And Here's Where You Can Get It.* So Yummy. https://soyummy.com/mcdon-alds-unexpected-dinner-meal/

Browne, R. (2019, November 25). *Web creator Tim Berners-Lee launches plan to "fix" the internet.* CNBC. https://www.cnbc.com/2019/11/25/tim-bern-ers-lee-launches-contract-for-the-web-to-fix-the-internet.html

Bryner, M. (2010, August 23). *What's the Biggest Animal in the World?* Live-science.Com. https://www.livescience.com/32780-whats-the-biggest-animal-in-the-world.html#:%7E:text=Its%20tongue%20alone%20 weighs%205%2C400,the%20largest%20babies%20on%20earth.

CBS News. (2011, January 5). *15 Most Bizarre Medical Treatments Ever.* https:// www.cbsnews.com/pictures/15-most-bizarre-medical-treatments-ever/2/

D. (2014a, March 1). *The President's Secret ZIP Code.* Dead Presidents. https://deadpresidents.tumblr.com/post/78147000455/the-presidents-secret-zip-code

Dearden, L. (2017, August 4). *Bulletproof armadillo puts Texas man in hospital after shot bounces off hard shell.* The Independent. https://www.independent.co.uk/news/world/americas/bulletproof-armadillo-puts-texas-man-hospital-after-shot-bounces-hard-shell-10432102.html

Deutsche Welle (www.dw.com). (n.d.). *A group of ravens makes a. . .* DW.COM. https://www.dw.com/en/what-do-you-call-a-group-of-ravens/a-18221414

Dhanaraj, J. (2016, November 23). *Woman calls police, upset over lack of sprinkles on ice cream.* The New Paper. https://tnp.straitstimes.com/news/woman-calls-police-upset-over-lack-sprinkles-ice-cream

DiNuzzo, E. (2019, April 10). *This Is Why Most Disney Characters Wear Gloves.* Reader's Digest. https://www.rd.com/article/why-do-disney-characters-wear-gloves/

Fernando, G. (2017, January 9). *What the hell does 'OK' stand for?* News. https://www.news.com.au/technology/science/evolution/what-the-hell-does-ok-stand-for/news-story/e65a0bad16107c887f97356e680329fc#:%7E:text=It's%20more%20correct%20to%20write,%2C%20or%20%E2%80%9Call%20correct%E2%80%9D.

Figuring Out the Largest Animal with NO Teeth! (n.d.). Science Bug Blog. http://sciencebug.org/blog/tag/blue-whale-facts/#:~:text=Scientists%20in%20Canada%20estimated%20that,pound%20(150%20ton)%20body!

Five interesting facts on the birthday of Martin Luther King Jr. (n.d.). The National Constitution Center. https://constitutioncenter.org/interactive-constitution/blog/five-interesting-facts-about-dr-martin-luther-king-jr-2#:%7E:text=Fact%201%3A%20King%20got%20a,public%20speaking%20at%20seminary%20school.&text=But%20in%20his%20first%20year,was%20valedictorian%20with%20straight%20A's.

Fries, W. C. (2009, July 17). *Cats and Dairy: Get the Facts.* WebMD. https://pets.webmd.com/cats/guide/cats-and-dairy-get-the-facts#1

Gaskill, M. (2018, October 24). *Roller Coasters were First Invented to Distract People from Immoral Behavior.* The Vintage News. https://www.thevintagenews.com/2018/10/24/roller-coasters/

Generator, M. (n.d.). *Humanimalia.* Humanimalia. https://humanimalia.org/

Giaimo, C. (2016, February 27). *NASA Stole the Rocket Countdown From a 1929 Fritz Lang Film*. Atlas Obscura. https://www.atlasobscura.com/articles/nasa-stole-the-rocket-countdown-from-a-1929-fritz-lang-film-1d569cc0-50ff-4045-b0c9-1f0d72a193db

Grundhauser, E. (2016, February 28). *The Dunce Cap Wasn't Always So Stupid*. Atlas Obscura. https://www.atlasobscura.com/articles/the-dunce-cap-wasnt-always-so-stupid#:%7E:text=The%20dunce%20cap%20has%20long,a%20symbol%20of%20respected%20scholars.

Higgins, E. (2021, October 22). *What Did People Do Before Toilet Paper?* Farmers' Almanac. https://www.farmersalmanac.com/before-toilet-paper-24419

The History Of Glitter. (n.d.). The Ransom Note. https://www.theransomnote.com/music/young-marco-takeover/the-history-of-glitter/

How Cows Eat Grass. (2021, August 18). U.S. Food and Drug Administration. https://www.fda.gov/animal-veterinary/animal-health-literacy/how-cows-eat-grass

I. (2014b, March 20). *Did you know you can't hold your nose and hum?* DiamondWellness.Com. https://diamondwellness.com/802/#:%7E:text=It%20is%20because%20when%20you,mouth%20and%20catch%20your%20breath.

Inge, S. (2015, May 5). *Italian astronaut has first espresso in space*. The Local Italy. https://www.thelocal.it/20150505/italian-astronaut-has-first-espresso-in-space

It's Flag Day. Here are some fun facts about the American flag you may not have known. (2020, June 14). FOX10 News. https://www.fox10tv.com/news/us_world_news/its-flag-day-here-are-some-fun-facts-about-the-american-flag-you-may-not/article_b1da5d64-12d4-5a87-9138-fb9d653f2cfc.html

Jain, S. (2019, October 16). *Why Do Passports Only Come In Four Colours?* NDTV.Com. https://www.ndtv.com/offbeat/why-do-passports-only-come-in-four-colours-2117697

Jones, M. (2019, April 4). *You Can Spell Every Number Up to 1,000 Without This Common Letter*. Reader's Digest. https://www.rd.com/article/spell-number-up-1000-without-a/

Jones, M. (2021a, July 16). *There's Only One Letter That's Not in Any U.S. State*

Name. Can You Guess It? Reader's Digest. https://www.rd.com/article/letter-not-in-any-state-name/

Jones, M. (2021b, July 19). *This Is the Only U.S. State Capital Without a Single McDonald's.* Reader's Digest. https://www.rd.com/article/state-capital-without-mcdonalds/

Joy, A. (2019, August 28). *"Albert Einstein" Is an Anagram for "Ten Elite Brains."* World Baba. https://worldbaba.blogspot.com/2019/08/albert-einstein-is-anagram-for-ten.html

Labor Pains. (n.d.). Slate Magazine. https://slate.com/gdpr?redirect_uri=%-2Farticles%2Farts%2Fpoem%2F2010%2F01%2Flabor_pains.html%3Fvia%3Dgdpr-consent&redirect_host=http%3A%2F%2Fwww.slate.com

Laliberte, M. (2018, June 6). *The Weird Reason Queen Elizabeth II's Cows Use Waterbeds.* Reader's Digest. https://www.rd.com/article/queen-elizabeth-cow-waterbeds/

Laliberte, M., & Taylor-Smith, J. (2021, October 13). *100 Fun and Interesting Facts About Practically Everything.* Reader's Digest. https://www.rd.com/list/interesting-facts/

Lambrechts, S. (2018, November 8). *Samsung built a robot butt just to test its smartphones' durability.* TechRadar. https://www.techradar.com/news/samsung-built-a-robot-butt-just-to-test-its-smartphones-durability

Leasca, S. (2018, October 20). *A Sloth Can Hold Its Breath for 40 Minutes Underwater — and 6 Other Facts For International Sloth Day.* Travel + Leisure. https://www.travelandleisure.com/animals/international-sloth-day

Locker, M. (2014, January 21). *Breaking Breakfast News: Froot Loops Are All the Same Flavor.* Time. https://time.com/1477/breaking-breakfast-news-froot-loops-are-all-the-same-flavor/

M. (n.d.). *How Long Can A Dolphin Hold Its Breath?* Ponce Inlet Watersports. https://ponceinletwatersports.com/how-long-can-a-dolphin-hold-its-breath/#:%7E:text=On%20average%2C%20dolphins%20can%20hold,oxygen%20needed%20to%20stay%20underwater

M.A. (2013a, October 11). *William McKinley Gave Away His Good Luck Charm (And Died).* KnowledgeNuts. https://knowledgenuts.com/2013/10/11/william-mckinley-gave-away-his-good-luck-charm-and-died/

MacRae, G. (2020, October 26). *Queen Elizabeth II has very own "body double" in bombshell 30 year Royal Family secret.* Express.Co.Uk. https://www.express.co.uk/news/royal/1352219/queen-elizabeth-II-body-double-melania-trump-royal-family-ella-slack-latest-updates-ont

Magazine, S. (n.d.). *Bananas Are Berries?* STANFORD Magazine. https://stanfordmag.org/contents/bananas-are-berries

Magazine, S. (2013a, May 1). *Never Underestimate the Power of a Paint Tube.* Smithsonian Magazine. https://www.smithsonianmag.com/arts-culture/never-underestimate-the-power-of-a-paint-tube-36637764/

Magazine, S. (2013b, June 18). *Why the Tomato Was Feared in Europe for More Than 200 Years.* Smithsonian Magazine. https://www.smithsonianmag.com/arts-culture/why-the-tomato-was-feared-in-europe-for-more-than-200-years-863735/#:%7E:text=In%20the%20late%201700s%2C%20a,were%20high%20in%20lead%20content

Martínez, M. (2020, September 17). *These five countries have no airport (because there's no space).* Ferrovial's Blog. https://blog.ferrovial.com/en/2018/04/these-five-countries-have-no-airport-because-theres-no-space/#:%7E:text=But%20there%20are%20a%20few,Vatican%20are%20States%20without%20airports.

Mercado, M. (2019, January 31). *Most Wasabi Isn't Real Wasabi, Which Is Actually Way More Rare & Expensive Than You Think.* Bustle. https://www.bustle.com/p/most-wasabi-isnt-real-wasabi-which-is-actually-way-more-rare-expensive-than-you-think-15914765#:%7E:text=Wasabi%20plants%20require%20very%20specific,don't%20know%20until%20now.

Merelli, A. (2016, October 7). *Adolf Hitler was nominated for the Nobel Peace Prize in a darkly ironic letter by Erik Gottfrid Christian Brandt.* Quartz. https://qz.com/803976/adolf-hitler-was-nominated-for-the-nobel-peace-prize-in-a-darkly-ironic-letter-by-erik-gottfrid-christian-brandt/

Mowke, D. (2016, December 30). *Which is the biggest single-celled organism?* Inshorts - Stay Informed. https://inshorts.com/en/news/which-is-the-biggest-singlecelled-organism-1483102816516

Mulraney, F. (2021, March 2). *All the pubs in Ireland used to be closed on St. Patrick's Day.* IrishCentral.Com. https://www.irishcentral.com/roots/history/all-pubs-ireland-closed-st-patricks-day

Muto, J. (2017, June 16). *What does H&M stand for?* TODAY.Com. https://www.today.com/style/what-does-h-m-stand-t112815

My Modern Met. (2017, August 1). *World's Oldest Bottle of Wine Remains Unopened Since the 4th Century.* https://mymodernmet.com/oldest-unopened-bottle-wine-world/#:%7E:text=So%2C%20how%20old%20is%20the,tomb%20in%20modern%2Dday%20Germany.

N. (2013b, May 1). *Uncommon Knowledge: What was the last letter added to the alphabet? -.* The Goods. https://www.uncommongoods.com/blog/2013/uncommon-knowledge-letter-added-alphabet/

The National Park - The world's biggest national park - [Visit Greenland!]. (2021a, May 11). Visit Greenland. https://visitgreenland.com/the-national-al-park/

The National Park - The world's biggest national park - [Visit Greenland!]. (2021b, May 11). Visit Greenland. https://visitgreenland.com/the-national-al-park/

NBC Universal. (2005, June 2). *Astronaut's hair sparks legal hubbub.* NBC News. https://www.nbcnews.com/id/wbna8062442

NPR Cookie Consent and Choices. (2011, June 2). Npr. https://choice.npr.org/index.html?origin=https://www.npr.org/sections/krulwich/2011/06/02/136860918/the-hardest-working-mom-on-the-planet?t=1610718604047

NPR Cookie Consent and Choices. (2015a, July 21). Npr. https://choice.npr.org/index.html?origin=https://www.npr.org/sections/thetwo-way/2015/07/21/424980378/winner-of-french-scrabble-title-does-not-speak-french

NPR Cookie Consent and Choices. (2015b, July 22). Npr. https://choice.npr.org/index.html?origin=https://www.npr.org/sections/thesalt/2015/07/22/425294957/how-an-11-year-old-boy-invented-the-popsicle

O. (2019a, November 1). *Thanks to 3D printing, NASA can basically "email" tools to astronauts.* The Brain Maze. https://thebrainmaze.com/thanks-to-3d-printing-nasa-can-basically-email-tools-to-astronauts/#:%7E:text=Technology-,Thanks%20to%203D%20printing%2C%20NASA,basically%20%E2%80%9Cemail%E2%80%9D%20tools%20to%20astronauts&text=Getting%20new%20equipment%20to%20the,a%20life%20or%20death%20matter.

Passy, J. (2019, October 21). *Here is the world's shortest (1.5 minutes) and longest (19.5 hours) commercial flight.* MarketWatch. https://www.marketwatch.

com/story/this-is-the-worlds-shortest-regularly-scheduled-flight-on-a-commercial-airline-2018-10-17#:%7E:text=Loganair%2C%20a%20Scottish%20regional%20airline,1.5%20minutes%20in%20the%20air.

Pez - The World's First Smoking Cessation Product. (2019, September 17). American Council on Science and Health. https://www.acsh.org/news/2019/09/16/pez-worlds-first-smoking-cessation-product-14284

Picard, C. (2021, August 14). *50 cool trivia facts to impress your friends.* Good Housekeeping. Retrieved October 26, 2021, from https://www.good-housekeeping.com/life/g25692093/random-trivia/.

Pictures: Colored Honey Made by Candy-Eating French Bees. (2021, May 3). Animals. https://www.nationalgeographic.com/animals/article/121011-blue-honey-honeybees-animals-science#:%7E:-text=Pictures%3A%20Colored%20Honey%20Made%20by%20Can-dy%2DEating%20French%20Bees&text=Beekeepers%20in%20northeastern%20France%20found,blue%20and%20green%20(pic-tured).&text=This%20honeycomb%20shows%20some%20of,one%20of%20the%20French%20beehives

Poppick, L. (2014, February 5). *Bumblebees Can Fly Higher Than Mount Everest.* Livescience.Com. https://www.livescience.com/43114-bumble-bees-fly-higher-mount-everest.html#:%7E:text=Alpine%20bumblebees%20have%20the%20ability,Everest%2C%20scientists%20have%20found.&-text=All%20of%20the%20bees%20were,the%20team%20reported%20Tuesday%20

Presidential Pet Museum. (n.d.). *Theodore Roosevelt's Hyena.* https://www.presi-dentialpetmuseum.com/theodore-roosevelts-hyena/

The Royal Family name. (2016, April 3). The Royal Family. https://www.royal.uk/royal-family-name

Rus, T. (2014, November 28). *Mercedes F200 Imagination: the joystick-controlled concept.* MercedesBlog. https://mercedesblog.com/mercedes-f200-imagi-nation-joystick-controlled-vehicle/

Russell, M. (2018, July 9). *Meet The ManhattAnts: Unique Species Of Ant Found Only In New York City.* The Rainforest Site News. https://blog.therainfor-estsite.greatergood.com/manhattant-species/#:%7E:text=Thank%20you!-,Meet%20The%20ManhattAnts%3A%20Unique%20Species%20Of%20Ant,Only%20In%20New%20York%20City&text=%E2%80%9CIt's%20a%20relative%20of%20the,entirely%20new%20species%20of%20ant

Saraniero, N. (2021, October 26). *10 Secrets of Yonkers Raceway at Empire City Casino*. Untapped New York. https://untappedcities.com/2017/03/14/daily-what-einsteins-eyeballs-are-in-a-safety-deposit-box-in-nyc/

Saunders, M. (2019, July 4). *The real Tinkerbell: don't mess with these tiny fairy wasps*. The Conversation. https://theconversation.com/the-real-tinkerbell-dont-mess-with-these-tiny-fairy-wasps-109796#:%7E:text=The%20smallest%20known%20insect%20of,found%20in%20the%20United%20States.

Scales, H. (n.d.). *How many hearts does an octopus have?* BBC Science Focus Magazine. https://www.sciencefocus.com/nature/why-does-an-octopus-have-more-than-one-heart/

Sea Cucumber - Holothuroidea. (2017, July 6). The Shape of Life | The Story of the Animal Kingdom. https://www.shapeoflife.org/news/featured-creature/2017/06/30/sea-cucumber-holothuroidea

Seager, C. (2019, August 21). *Facepaint, champagne and antelope skin – writers' oddball quirks revealed*. The Guardian. https://www.theguardian.com/books/2015/jul/23/facepaint-champagne-and-antelope-skin-writers-oddball-quirks-revealed#:%7E:text=TS%20Eliot%20wore%20green%20makeup%20and%20lipstick%20when%20he%20wrote&text=Quite%20why%20he%20assumed%20a%20green%20pallor%2C%20nobody%20knew.&text=His%20biographer%2C%20Peter%20Ackroyd%2C%20agreed,rather%20than%20a%20bank%20official.%E2%80%9D

Sehra, S. (2016, June 16). *Eiffel Tower gets taller by 6 inches in summer*. Inshorts - Stay Informed. https://inshorts.com/en/news/eiffel-tower-gets-taller-by-6-inches-in-summer-1466096019720

Shamsian, J. (2019, July 2). *Here's why your pants have a teeny tiny pocket that's too small to use*. Insider. https://www.insider.com/small-pocket-pants-jeans-watch-2018-03

Sharp, T. (2018, May 22). *World's First Commercial Airline | The Greatest Moments in Flight*. Space.Com. https://www.space.com/16657-worlds-first-commercial-airline-the-greatest-moments-in-flight.html#:%7E:text=Pheil%2C%20former%20mayor%20of%20St,an%20aviation%20entrepreneur%20from%20St.

The shortest war in history: The Anglo-Zanzibar War of 1896. (n.d.). The Historical Association. https://www.history.org.uk/secondary/resource/7950/the-shortest-war-in-history-the-anglo-zanzibar-wa#:%7E:text=At%209am%20on%2027%20August,Palace%20and%20Harem%20in%20Zanzibar.

Should I Worry About How Hot My Engine Is Running? (n.d.). Cars.Com. https://www.cars.com/articles/should-i-worry-about-how-hot-my-engine-is-running-1420680334271/#:%7E:text=For%20most%20cars%2C%20the%20normal,normal%20range%20in%20the%20middle

Simpson, J. (2017, July 18). *The British Perfected the Art of Brewing Tea Inside an Armored Vehicle*. War Is Boring. https://warisboring.com/the-british-perfected-the-art-of-brewing-tea-inside-an-armored-vehicle/#:%7E:text=Tank%20crewmen%20had%20to%20stop,one%20disastrous%20World%20War%20II.

Sinha, S. (2020, November 5). *Microwave Was An Accident, And The Inventor Was Paid Only $2 For It!* Global Youth Voice. https://www.globalyouthvoice.com/microwave-oven/#:%7E:text=Spencer%20has%20over%20300%20patents,Edison%20and%20the%20Wright%20Brothers.

Staff, S. X. (2008, October 17). *Blue bananas: Ripening bananas glow an intense blue under black light*. Phys.Org. https://phys.org/news/2008-10-blue-bananas-ripening-intense-black.html#:%7E:text=Under%20normal%20light%2C%20these%20natural,ripening%20bananas%20appear%20blue%20instead.&text=The%20intensity%20of%20the%20luminescence,progress%2C%20the%20blue%20glow%20decreases

Stage, C. (2017, April 5). *Ludwig van Beethoven: An Overview*. Center Stage Music Center. https://centerstagemusiccenter.com/ludwig-van-beethoven-an-overview/

Stanek, B. (2017, May 24). *Scientists may have finally figured out how flamingos can stand on one leg, not fall over*. The Week. https://theweek.com/speedreads/701166/scientists-may-have-finally-figured-how-flamingos-stand-leg-not-fall-over

Statue of Liberty Lighthouse. (n.d.). LighthouseFriends. https://lighthousefriends.com/light.asp?ID=581

Sticking their necks out for evolution: Why sloths and manatees have unusually long (or short) necks. (n.d.). ScienceDaily. https://www.sciencedaily.com/releases/2011/05/110505212314.htm

The shortest railways in the world take less than a Minute. Best Travel Tale. (2020, February 21). Retrieved October 26, 2021, from https://besttraveltale.com/travel/the-shortest-railways-in-the-world-take-less-than-a-minute/.

The Swearing-In of the First Woman Elected to Congress, Representative Jeannette Rankin of Montana | US House of Representatives: History, Art & Archives. (n.d.). History, Art & Archives. https://history.house.gov/Historical-Highlights/1901-1950/The-swearing-in-of-the-first-woman-elected-to-Congress,-Representative-Jeannette-Rankin-of-Montana/

The Terminator: James Cameron's HUGE Mistake To Direct The Movie. (2020, January 29). Screen Rant. https://screenrant.com/terminator-movie-cameron-screenplay-sold-one-dollar/

U.T. (2014c, September 29). *USA TODAY*. Newser. https://eu.usatoday.com/story/news/nation/2014/09/29/secret-starbucks-cia/16430023/

V. (2020b, July 5). *Shell-shaped gas station in Winston-Salem, North Carolina*. Silly America. https://sillyamerica.com/blog/shell-shaped-gas-station-in-winston-salem-north-carolina/

Villazon, L. (n.d.). *Can a human produce a sound outside the human audible range?* BBC Science Focus Magazine. https://www.sciencefocus.com/the-human-body/can-a-human-produce-a-sound-outside-the-human-audible-range/#:%7E:text=But%20a%20few%20individuals%20have,t%20be%20heard%2C%20only%20felt.

W. (2019b, October 1). *How Many Balls Are Used at Wimbledon?* WDH. https://www.wimbledondebentureholders.com/articles/2019/10/01/how-many-balls-used-wimbledon/#:%7E:text=Because%20of%20the%20effect%20of,they%20aren't%20worn%20down.

Website, T. O. E. T. (2021, February 1). *How did they build the Tower so quickly?* La Tour Eiffel. https://www.toureiffel.paris/en/news/130-years/how-did-they-build-tower-so-quickly

Where is Earth's Largest Waterfall? (n.d.). National Ocean Service. https://oceanservice.noaa.gov/facts/largest-waterfall.html

Which Came First: Orange the Color or Orange the Fruit? (2012, February 8). Mental Floss. https://www.mentalfloss.com/article/29942/which-came-first-orange-color-or-orange-fruit

Your supermarket apples may be 10 months old. (2017, April 8). Business Insider. https://www.businessinsider.com/supermarket-apples-10-months-old-2017-4?r=US&IR=T#:%7E:text=That%20apple%20you%20just%20ate,harvested%20from%20August%20to%20November.&text=Apples%20that%20will%20be%20sold%20later%20go%20to%20controlled%20atmosphere%20storage.

(2015a, December 23). *Were Lunar Volcanoes Active When Dinosaurs Roamed the Earth?* Universe Today. https://www.universetoday.com/115245/were-lunar-volcanoes-active-when-dinosaurs-roamed-the-earth/

(2015b, December 24). *Why Are Lunar Shadows So Dark?* Universe Today. https://www.universetoday.com/93991/why-are-lunar-shadows-so-dark/#:%7E:text=On%20the%20Moon%20there%20is,where%20sunlight%20hits%2C%20very%20bright.&text=It%20tends%20to%20reflect%20light,seen%20in%20Apollo%20mission%20photographs.

Made in the USA
Middletown, DE
23 November 2022

15878818R00050